I'M BUSY, TOO

Norma Simon   *Pictures by* Dora Leder

ALBERT WHITMAN & COMPANY, MORTON GROVE, ILLINOIS

For my editor,
my inspiration and my dear friend, Caroline Rubin,
with gratitude.

Library of Congress Cataloging-in-Publication Data

Simon, Norma.
 I'm busy, too.

 (A Concept book)
 SUMMARY: Three preschoolers and their families
have busy days at school and work.
 [1. Schools—Fiction. 2. Day care centers—Fiction.
3. Work—Fiction.] I. Leder, Dora. II. Title.
PZ7.S6053lm   [E]   79-18374
ISBN 0-8075-3464-1

Text © 1980 by Norma Simon.
Illustrations © 1980 by Dora Leder.
Published in 1980 by Albert Whitman & Company,
6340 Oakton Street, Morton Grove, Illinois 60053.
Published simultaneously in Canada
by General Publishing, Limited, Toronto.

Printed in the United States of America.
10   9   8   7   6   5   4

A Note About This Book

Many young children attend nurseries, Headstart programs, child-care centers, play schools, or kindergartens. Whatever they are called, these are all child-sized, child-centered worlds in which children work and enjoy being with other children.

While parents and other family members are busy at their work, these young children are busy, too. For play is the child's work, an important process by which young minds and bodies develop and grow.

For many children, attending school often results in the first long separation from parents and home. On their own in school, boys and girls have the opportunity to develop a sense of themselves as people apart from their families. They find they have independent abilities to work, communicate, make friends, create, explore, and discover.

Parents and teachers should build strong bridges between home and school. When children sense that the adults around them value their schoolwork, they place greater value on it themselves. The whole family can establish positive attitudes toward school and make an effort to participate in school life.

Mikey, Sara, and Charlie, the children in this book, are part of the busy working world "all over town." While their families are different, the routines in their homes and the caring attitudes found there have much in common. These children have a lot to share at the end of their school day. When grownups listen to what children say, they acknowledge how much they value their children's accomplishments.

NORMA SIMON

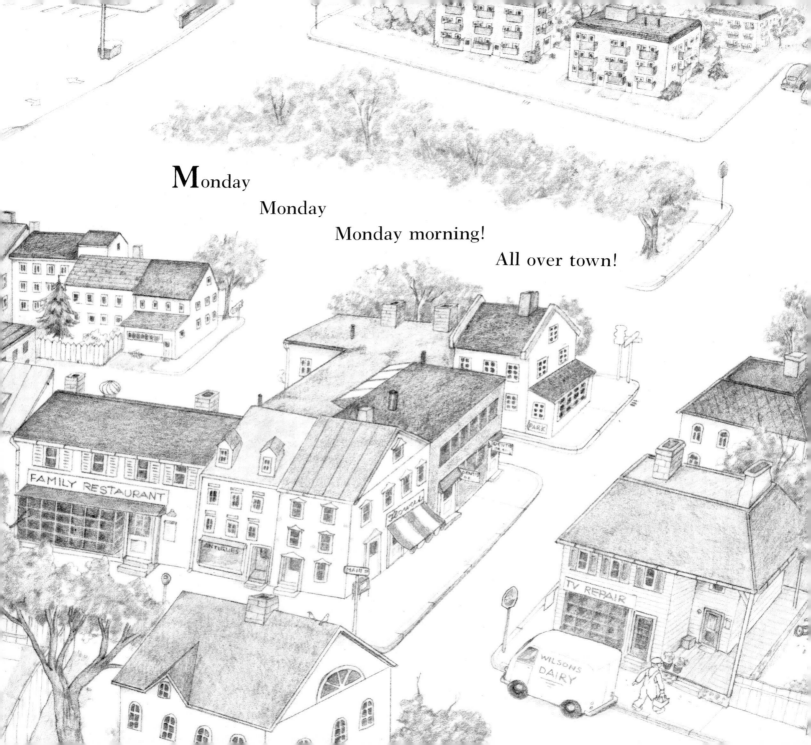

Monday
Monday
Monday morning!
All over town!

"Time to get up!"
calls Mikey's mother.

"Time to get up!"
calls Sara's sister.

"Time to get up!"
calls Charlie's dad.

Stretching,
yawning,
grumbling,
tumbling,
tossing covers off,
all over town.

Washing hands
and washing faces,

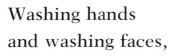

getting dressed
and tying laces.

Toast pops
up from toasters,

coffee cups fill
steamy and brown.

It's Monday-morning
breakfast time
all over town!

"I'm ready for work,"
says Mikey's mother.
"Me, too," says Mikey.
"Soon as I brush my teeth."

"Ready to go?"
Sara asks her sister.
"In a minute," Sister says.
"I have to get my books."

"Ready, Charlie?" asks his father.
"Ready and steady," Charlie tells him.
"Race you to the bus."

Going to work,
going to school,
everybody's coming, going
all over town!

Mikey's mother drops him off,
Sara's sister takes her in.
Charlie's first off the bus,
all ready for school.

Children coming into school,
teachers waiting for the children,
ready for the busy workday,
ready to be busy, busy.

Talking
        singing,
jumping
        climbing,
painting
        building.

Indoors
        outdoors,
outdoors
        indoors,
working
        playing,
playing
        working,
          all
            day
              long.

Work on Monday,
  work on Tuesday.
      Wednesday
        Thursday
          Friday
            workdays.

Children, teachers,
teachers, children,
busy, busy,
working hard.

What does Mikey do today?
Draws a picture of a pumpkin,
makes a mask for Halloween.

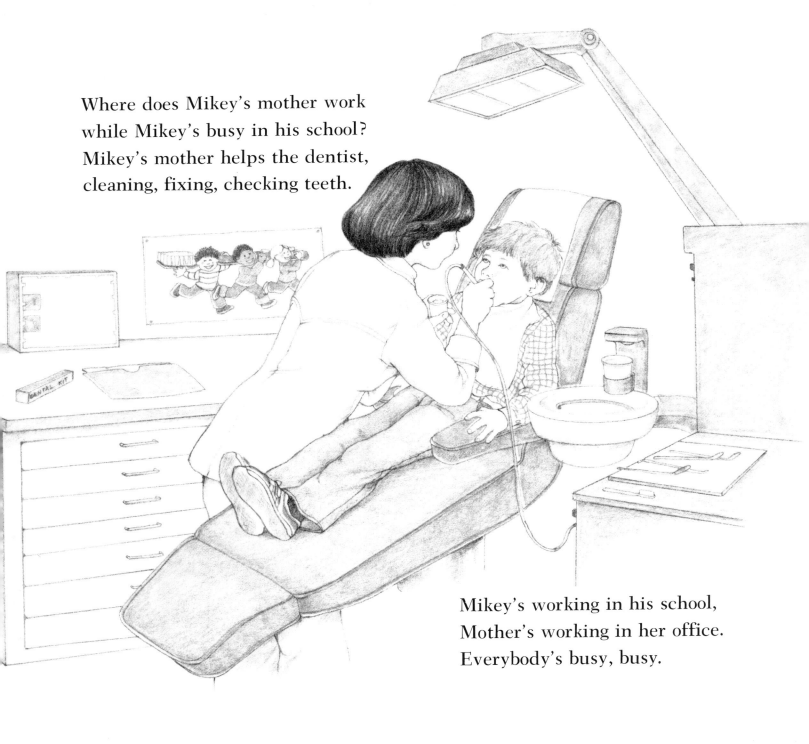

Where does Mikey's mother work
while Mikey's busy in his school?
Mikey's mother helps the dentist,
cleaning, fixing, checking teeth.

Mikey's working in his school,
Mother's working in her office.
Everybody's busy, busy.

What does Charlie do in school?
Builds with blocks,
builds with friends,
builds a garage
and a long, long road.

Where does Charlie's father work
while Charlie's busy in his school?
Father's working in his shop,
fixing broken TV sets.

Charlie's working in his school,
Father's working in his shop.
Everybody's busy, busy.

What does Sara do in school?
Mixes paints,
paints some pictures,
hangs her pictures up to dry.

Where does Sara's family work
while Sara's busy in her school?

Mother's working in their house,
cleaning, shopping, cooking, sewing,
taking good care of baby.

Father's working in his restaurant,
shopping, baking, cooking, serving,
making sure the food is good.

Sister's working in her school,
reading, writing, thinking, learning.
Boys and girls working hard.

Sara's working in her school,
Sara's family's working, too.
Everybody's busy, busy
all over town!

Mikey's mother picks him up
after school, after work.

Charlie's father waits for Charlie
after school, after work.

Sara's sister picks her up
after school for both of them.

Now's a time to be at home,
now's a time to talk together.

"Another busy day?"
Mikey's mother asks.

"I made a mask for Halloween.
Can I be a pirate?"

"I'll help you make your costume," Mikey's mother says.

"Oh, Sara, such fine paintings!"
Her mother holds them up.

"Let's hang them in our room."
Her sister smiles at Sara.

"How was your day, Charlie?
Busy, like mine?"

"We built a garage
for Mikey's truck.
I was busy, too."

"I wish I could have seen it," Charlie's father tells him.
"I'll visit school one day soon. Then you can show me everything."

Sleepy people, tired people,
washing up to go to bed.
Kissing, hugging, tucking in.

"See you in the morning,"
Mikey's mother says.

"I'll come to bed soon,"
Sara's sister calls.

"Goodnight, son,"
Charlie's father says.

Happy dreams,
     all over town.